Ama's Gift

Ama's Gift

Copyright © 2020 Kamapala Chukwuka

Layout and typesetting: Hatice Bayramoglu

Illustrations: Jose Gutierrez & Hatice Bayramoglu

ISBN 978-1-8382654-0-3

Publisher Inspired Creative Hub
Contact : www.inspiredcreativehub.com
info@inspiredcreativehub.com
kamchuks12@gmail.com

Please visit www.kamapalac.com to contact Kamapala for school visits or speaking engagements

This book belongs to

_____

You are beautiful and gifted.
Don't let fear or what others think stop
you from sharing your gifts with the world.
Your gifts make you unique and by sharing them,
you make the world beautiful &
magical - so please keep sharing.

Every time Ama sang, her singing was so beautiful that it brought tears to her parents' eyes.

Ama's parents loved hearing their daughter's voice so much that they encouraged her to sing loud and strong—so everyone could hear her.

Ama's mum often joked that her daughter's voice was so beautiful that even the flowers bloomed when she sang!

Ama loved to sing, but she was only happy singing for her parents.

Her mum encouraged her, "Ama, you have the most beautiful voice! I'm sure everyone would love to hear it!"

Her dad reassured her, "I'll be right there with you, cheering loudly on the day you decide to sing for everyone."

But nothing they said could change Ama's mind.

Ama wanted to share her voice with her friends and the rest of her family, but she was scared.

The thought of singing in front of everyone made her very nervous.

Ama knew that her parents loved her voice,
and she also loved her voice. But what if no one else did?

What if her friends
didn't find her
voice beautiful?

What if they laughed at her? What if she jumbled up the words while singing?

All of these thoughts worried her.

So, she decided that she would sing only for her parents. And that would be good enough for her.

But would it really be good enough? Ama wondered.

Would she ever *live out her dream*
of singing in front of the whole school one day?

Oh, if she could only find the courage,
that would be the most *amazing feeling!*

As the days went by, Ama became
more and more discouraged—until
she didn't want to sing at all.

That made Ama and her parents sad.

The big school talent show was fast approaching,
and singing would have been Ama's showcase talent.

"Ah," she sighed. If only I could be brave enough to sing at the talent show!

If she couldn't sing, what else could Ama do?

As the talent show drew closer,
Ama had a dream one night.
A Fairy Angel appeared to her and said,
"My dear Ama, you are a bright and
confident girl!"

"That beautiful gift
you have—that magical voice—wasn't given
to you to keep all to yourself."

"You received this gift to share with everyone you know."

"Every time you sing, you make the world more beautiful!"

"Whenever you sing, you share happiness, hope, and love."

"Ama, don't let fear stop you from sharing your gift."

"Share your voice, and you'll see how much of a difference you can make!"

Ama awoke from her dream with *joy* and **excitement**.

Now she knew what she had to do; she had to sing in the talent show. It was time to share her gift with everyone.

The big day arrived, and it was
Ama's turn to perform.

TALENT
Show

She walked onto the stage. Her heart
was beating faster than ever before,
her hands were sweating, and her knees were shaking.

She wanted to run off the stage, but everyone
was staring at her now.
It was too late to turn back.

At that moment, she thought about
what the Fairy Angel had said.

And she remembered why it was important
to share her gift with the world.

Taking a long, deep breath, Ama closed her
eyes, opened her mouth, and began to sing.

At first, her singing was barely audible, even to herself. But then she opened her heart and allowed the joy of singing to take over.

Her voice was so beautiful that it brought tears of joy to people's eyes.

At the end of her song, the audience jumped to their feet—cheering loudly.

Ama had done it! She had shared her gift.

Her dream of performing in front of the whole school had come true!

She was proud of herself. She had managed to do it, even though she was scared.

Her friends and family were amazed and delighted for her. But most of all, they were proud of her!

It was clear to Ama that sharing her gift made her happy and made others happy, too.

Ama decided that from now on, she would boldly share her voice every chance she got.

She wasn't going to let fear stop her, ever again.

Sharing her gift was fun and exciting, and she loved it!

Hello, my friend the Fairy Angel says we all have gifts/talents within us.

A gift or talent is something we are naturally good at doing. My gift/talent is singing. Here is a table of other examples of gifts/talents, can you find yours?

Building/ construction (Lego, puzzles	Sports/ athletics/ playing football/tennis	Arts & Crafts - Drawing, painting, making arty stuff
Good with numbers / Maths	Organising stuff / Neat & tidy	Singing
Drama/Acting/ Poetry	Inspiring and motivating others	Being positive
Baking /cooking	Gymnastics	Reading / Writing
Making friends	Ballet	Solving problems
Helping others	Dancing	Creativity
Thinking/debating	Music/playing musical instruments	Teaching
Caring for others	Photography	Technology/ IT

Head over to www.kamapalac.com **to see many more gifts/talents**

Let's have some fun with these questions

1. What was Ama's gift or talent?
2. Do you remember why she didn't want to share with anyone other than her parents?
3. Why did the Fairy Angel say it was important for Ama to share her gift?
4. How did Ama feel after sharing her gift?
5. Do you have a special gift? How do you go about sharing it with others?

Other books by the Author

Mummy's love for you will always be

Upcoming titles

Emeka's Big Heart
Chima's Reddy
Makena's attitude of gratitude

About the Author

Kamapala Chukwuka is a mum of 3 boys. A certified confidence coach dedicated to empowering women and young people find their greatness and live it out daily. She is also the founder of a Creative Digital Agency(Inspiredcreativehub.com) & a motivational speaker.

Kamapala is passionate about publishing Children's Books that shine a positive light on black characters & empower black children to see themselves as confident, capable, loving, kind & all round fabulous.

Dear Reader,

Ama's gift is a book I really enjoyed writing. I hope it came across and you loved reading it too.

Would you be ever so kind to leave me a review on Amazon & consider sharing with others.

Could you share a photo or 2 on social media & tag me? I love seeing your photos & reading your words. They inspire me to keep sharing my gift of writing.

I would be delighted to see all your beautiful colouring of Ama so please do share with me as well.

You can find me on Instagram & Facebook as **@kamapala_c**

Visit my website for fun activities, inspiration & updates

I'm available for **Author visits**, **Library/group zoom calls + visits**
I'm also available for **motivational talks** on confidence contact me : **kamapalac@gmail.com**

Printed by Amazon Italia Logistica S.r.l.
Torrazza Piemonte (TO), Italy